ALL
ENTER HERE...
ABANDON HOPE
...OF KEEPING
A STRAIGHT FACE!

This is
Neuman's
Inferno

...WHERE ALL THE LITTLE
MAD DEVILS RAISE HELL WITH

The Establishment

AND GET EVERYBODY

"BURNING MAD"

William M. Gaines's
BURNING

ALBERT B. FELDSTEIN, Editor

WARNER BOOKS

A Warner Communications Company

ON A
SATURDAY
AFTERNOON

7

Hmmm! That guy ought to be **ashamed** of himself! **Imagine!** A grown man refusing to play "Piggyback" with his own three-year-old son!!

"Piggyback, Da, Da! PIGGYBACK!!" I tell you—I can't **stand** it any longer!!

MOVIE DIALOGUE WE'D LIKE TO HEAR

A COLLECTION OF "REVERSE CLICHES"

DESIGNED TO INJECT NEW LIFE INTO OLD "SURE-FIRE DIALOGUE"

ARTIST:
GEORGE
WOODBRIDGE
WRITER: HARRY PURVIS

See that boy behind the counter—the one jerking sodas? I discovered him when he was just a star at one of the biggest studios in Hollywood!

THE REJEC

Editor
MAD Magazine
New York, New York

Dear Sir:

Upon bringing to a close my career as an unsuccessful cartoonist I find that my voluminous collection of rejection slips does not include one of yours (see sketch below).

Would you be kind enough to send me a MAD rejection slip and thus complete my collection? Thanks very much.

Sincerely,

Tom Hudson

RESERVED FOR "MAD"

TION SLIP

WRITER AND ARTIST: TOM HUDSON

Dear Mr. Hudson:

We found your idea for "Rejection Slips From Various Magazines" highly amusing and have assigned the article to one of our regular writers.

We are pleased to enclose a check in payment.

Cordially,

Albert B. Feldstein

Albert B. Feldstein,

Editor

Editor
MAD Magazine
New York, New York

Dear Sir:

Thanks for the check, but please, please
could you spare me one rejection slip?

As my wife would say,"Is my 'slip' showing?"

Haha. (see sketch).

MEMO

FROM:
William M. Gaines
Publisher

TO:
Al Feldstein
Editor

Dear Al:
Just happened to run across that "slip-showing" cartoon while nosing around your desk. I think it would make a great cover painting...with Alfred standing on some big fat dame's slip at a real fancy costume ball, and looking out at the reader with his typical "What--me worry?" grin. What do you think?

Bill

P.S. Will you see that a check is sent to Hudson for this cover idea.

Editor
MAD Magazine
New York, New York

Dear Sir:

I am afraid that you have missed the
point of the whole thing. My letter was
a request for you to send me one of your
rejection slips and not intended to be a
contribution to your magazine.

I'm still looking! (see sketch)

Sincerely,

Tom Hudson

Dear Mr. Hudson:

Thank you for sending us your delightful "Mail Box" cartoon. We all enjoyed it very much, and plan to use it as the new heading for our "Letters Dept."

Enclosed, please find our check in payment.

Sincerely,

Al Feldstein

Al Feldstein,
Editor

Dear Tom:

Your hilarious "Drive-In Movie" cartoon broke up the entire office, and served as a springboard for a "Drive-In Movie" article.

Enclosed please find check in payment. You're doing great! Keep those ideas coming!

MAD-ly yours,

al

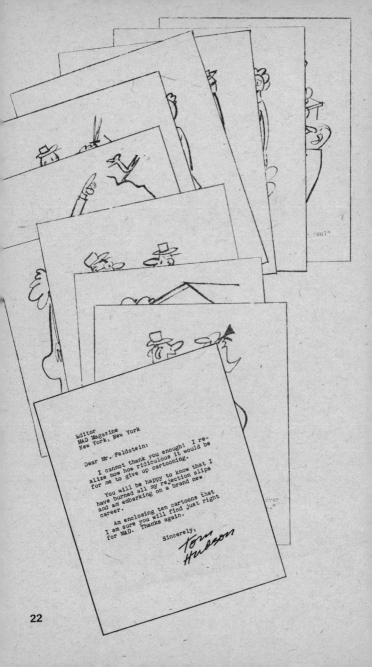

Editor
MAD Magazine
New York, New York

Dear Mr. Feldstein:

I cannot thank you enough! I realize now how ridiculous it would be
for me to give up cartooning.

You will be happy to know that I
have burned all my rejection slips
and am embarking on a brand new
career.

I am enclosing ten cartoons that
I am sure you will find just right
for MAD. Thanks again.

Sincerely,

Tom
Hudson

MAD

THE EDITORS REGRET
THAT THE ENCLOSED
MATERIAL IS NOT
SUITABLE FOR OUR
CURRENT NEEDS.

ROASTED PEANUTS DEPT.

One of the popular best-sellers of the past year has been a charming little book by the creator of "Peanuts," Charles M. Schulz, called "Happiness Is A Warm Puppy." Using his "Peanuts" characters, Mr. Schulz explores the little things of childhood that bring happiness. For example: "Happiness is walking on the grass in your bare feet," "Happiness is three friends in a sand box ... with no fighting," "Happiness is a bread and butter sandwich folded over," etc. Which is all very well if you remember childhood being full of happiness. We at MAD have the distinct recollection of childhood being pretty miserable. So here is our version of how the rest of the comic strip kid-characters would show the other side of the coin in this MAD children's book called ...

MISERY IS A COLD HOT DOG

ARTIST: BOB CLARKE   **WRITER: LARRY SIEGEL**

Misery is an overcoat
that has to last for
two seasons.

Misery is a classmate
screeching nails
on a blackboard.

Misery is your
ball down the sewer.

Misery is a knot
in your hair.

Misery is landing on *Boardwalk* with a *hotel*, just when you've gotten enough money to afford a house on *Ventnor Avenue*.

Misery is moving.

Misery is eating a peanut butter sandwich with braces on your teeth.

Misery is
no skate key.

Misery is an ice cream pop
falling off the stick.

Misery is a
sister.

Misery is
having to
share.

Misery is finding
your pet goldfish
floating.

Misery is the
skinny end
of your tie
sticking out.

Misery is a left-handed kid sitting next
to you, whose paper is impossible to copy
from, during a test.

29

Misery is the first
snowfall of Winter—
and you have a cold.

Misery is getting lost
at the beach.

Misery is a piece of
birthday cake with
no flower.

Misery is crayons
left out in the sun.

Misery is being dressed up
and waiting an hour before
the rest of the family is
ready to go out.

Misery is
Milk of Magnesia.

Misery is finding a
squashed banana in
your school lunch bag.

Misery is walking in the grass in your bare feet—
and then discovering you're in a cow pasture.

Misery is a
tongue-depressor.

Misery is coming home from the beach
and sitting on hot plastic auto seat
covers wearing nothing but swim trunks.

Misery is a
roll of damp caps.

Misery is having to change
out of a wet bathing suit
under a towel at the beach.

M isery is a
rectal thermometer.

M isery is getting clothes
instead of toys
for Christmas.

Misery is
trying on
clothes.

Misery is a wet kiss
on the face by an
aunt with a mustache.

Misery is having to eat
the watery part of a
loose soft-boiled egg.

Misery is a sun-burned back, and
then not being able to reach the
good spots when it starts peeling.

Misery is buying five baseball gum cards and getting five Marv Throneberrys of the New York Mets.

Misery is when your parents won't let you keep a kitten you found.

Misery is coming home with a rip in your best suit.

RUSSIAN "RUSSIAN ROULETTE"

ARTIST & WRITER: SERGIO ARAGONES

1

2

3

4

CLICK!

5

6

CLICK!

38

7

8

CLICK!

9

10

CLICK.

39

11

12 POW!

A few years ago (in MAD #49), we ran an article called "A Best Seller Hits The Commercial Trail." In it, we showed how a popular best-selling book is exploited so that it makes a fortune in other areas: i.e., product merchandising, TV shows, Broadway musicals, record albums, etc. Now, three-and-a-half years later, in line with MAD's steady progress in a backward direction, we are going to show you how a book becomes a best seller in the first place. Mainly, here is MAD's version of . . .

HOW A
BEST-SELLER
IS BORN

ARTIST: JOE ORLANDO   WRITER: LARRY SIEGEL

41

44

There's nothing more exciting for a publisher than to be able to put out a book which is so hot that he can announce in his ads: **"JUST PUBLISHED! AND ALREADY IN ITS THIRD PRINTING!"**...

The dream of every author and publisher is to have their book become a selection of the "The Book Of The Week Club." This indicates that the book is of great literary value . . .

Congratulations, Mr. Doubledeal! We on "The Book Of The Week Club" Selection Board have decided that "The Polio Vaccine Coloring Book" is bad enough to be included in next week's Club Selections!

Wonderful! I was sweating it out! You fellows corner the market on atrocious books, and I was worried that some of you actually thought our book was good!

BOARD ROOM

Once in a rare while, a publisher comes up with a great book which lends itself perfectly to a motion picture treatment. If he plays his cards right, he might sell it to a canny Hollywood producer . . .

Darryl, you fellows in Hollywood haven't had an original screenplay idea for 20 years, and you'll buy anything in print for adaptation. Well, we've got a new book coming out soon— by Dr. Jonah Sauk here, —which will make a great movie!

Sold! I'll pay you a half-million dollars—in small, unmarked bills, the way you like it—and then you tell me the name of the book, okay?

And while we're waiting for the money, why not take a walk around the lot and watch my latest movie being made?

TITANIC STUDIOS

DARRYL F. SPORTZ EXECUTIVE

47

Before a book is published, we take our author to many scintillating cocktail parties where he meets all the important people on the American literary scene. It's wonderful for prestige purposes . . .

I read your latest book, Steve . . . "Ace Crossword Puzzles"! Loved it! Tell me, was any part of it autobiographical?

Yes—17 Across on page 34 . . . and 42 Down on page 91!

What do you find to be the underlying philosophy in Sandra Dee's new book, "Hair Styles In A Nuclear Age"?

Man's inhumanity to man! But it was all said before—and better—in "Dating And Personal Tips For Teenagers" by Yogi Berra

Whenever a new book comes out, we try to place our author on a few select quality TV shows to plug it. We always handle this publicity with taste and care.

This is the 58th TV show Dr. Sauk has appeared on this week to plug his new book! Where will it all end?

I hear he appears as a guest cartoon character on "The Flintstones" next —and that's it!

DR. SAUKS POLIO VACCIN COLORING BOOK

48

We also have our author appear at important, carefully selected book centers to autograph copies of his book.

I'll go to **any** length to stock my library with great literature, Dr. Sauk! That's why I'm so glad they're giving your book away **free** with every purchase of 5 cans of Schneiderman's Tuna Fish!

I hear they also sell this book at regular book stores! What's a **book store**, Selig?

Search me! I think it's one of those places down the block where they sell greeting cards!

FREE! AUTOGRAPHED COPY OF **DR. SAUK'S** POLIO VACCINE COLORING BOOK

One of the happiest moments in a publisher's life is when he can use the following blurb in his ads: **"750,000 COPIES NOW IN PRINT."**...

Here's tomorrow's ad for ''The Polio Vaccine Coloring Book'', Mr. Doubledeal—just as you ordered. At the top, it says **"750,000 COPIES NOW IN PRINT!"**...

Good! Just don't tell anybody that we've only sold **16** of those 750,000 copies so far!!

And of course it's a great thrill for a publisher and an author to walk past a book shop and see their book on prominent display in the window . . .

For one thing, we are even **more** careful than he is in not tampering with the author's work and integrity . . .

Mr. Hopper, you know of course what happened to my last book! It was a disgrace! Well, I've written a new book entitled **"Polio Vaccine And Its Contribution to Humanity"**! I've come to you with it because I **know** you won't resort to the same methods as Mr. Doubledeal . . .

A wise move, Dr. Sauk. Yes, I think it was dreadful the way he turned your brilliant medical treatise into a disgusting coloring book. I don't believe in such ridiculous things as coloring books, especially when the author's an esteemed personage such as you! No, sir what I have in mind is:

A PHOTO CAPTION BOOK!!

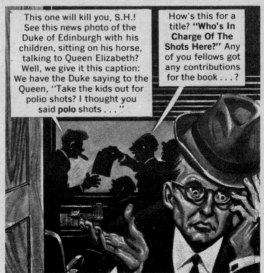

This one will kill you, S.H.! See this news photo of the Duke of Edinburgh with his children, sitting on his horse, talking to Queen Elizabeth? Well, we give it this caption: We have the Duke saying to the Queen, "Take the kids out for polio shots? I thought you said **polo** shots . . ."

How's this for a title? **"Who's In Charge Of The Shots Here?"** Any of you fellows got any contributions for the book . . . ?

We could've done this next article as a "Baseball Coloring Book," but everybody's doing Coloring Books! And we could've done this article as a "Baseball Photo-Caption Book," but everybody's doing Photo-Caption Books. So we've decided to do it as a "Primer" which nobody's doing yet. Except us! We've done them...and done them...and done them! It may not be an original format, but it's seasonal. And so, with the cry of "Play ball!" being heard throughout the land...followed by the cry of "So what!", we proudly present...

THE MAD
BASEBALL
PRIMER

ARTIST: JACK RICKARD   WRITER: STAN HART

THE GREAT
AMERICAN
PASTIME

Easy Little Steps To Help You Get To First Base

Lesson 1.
THE BALLPARK

See the ballpark.
The expensive seats are down front.
When the sun shines, the people in them sweat.
When it rains, the people in them get wet.
This is known as soaking the rich.
Walk up the ramp to *your* seat.
Pass the 1st tier. Pass the 2nd tier.
When you get to the top, hear the announcer.
He says, "Is there a doctor in the house?"
That's because you've just had a heart attack!

See the teams come out on the field.
Do not bother to wave "hello" to the ballplayers.
They will not wave back.
They cannot see you.
Wave "hello" to the passing airplanes.
The pilots will wave back.
They *can* see you!
How will you know what's happening down on the field?
Simple! Listen to the game on your portable radio!

Lesson 2.
THE BASEBALL PLAYER

See the baseball player.
He plays ball every day.
People consider him a hero.
You play ball every day, too.
People consider you a bum.
Everyone loves the baseball player.
People chip in money to give him a special night.
People who make $85 a week,
The baseball player makes $75,000 a year.
Aren't people a little mixed up?

Watch the baseball player on television.
Some read commercials off "idiot cards."
Some don't. They can't read at all!
Most kids want to be baseball players when they grow up.
What do baseball players want to be when they grow up?

Lesson 3.
THE BASEBALL FAN

See the baseball fan.
He knows the names of all the baseball players.
He doesn't know the names of his children.
The baseball fan has a head for figures.
He knows everyone's batting average.
He doesn't know his own telephone number.
He knows the 3rd-string catcher for the Mets.
He doesn't know who Kennedy is.
The baseball fan is over 21.
He can vote in elections.
He can sit on juries.
It makes you stop and think!

Lesson 4.
THE SPORTSWRITER

See the sportswriter.
The sportswriter doesn't go to the game.
He goes to a bar and watches it on TV.
The sportswriter drinks like a man.
But he writes like a child.

Lesson 5.
THE SPORTSCASTER

See the sportscaster.
The sportscaster must go to every game.
He tells you what you are watching.
He makes dull games sound exciting.
Turn off the TV picture.
Turn up the TV sound.
Isn't baseball exciting?

Lesson 6.

THE KNOTHOLE GANG

See the kids in the ballpark.
The kind management lets them in for free.
No one else wants to see the 10th-place team play.
The management wants to keep the kids off the street.
Because on the streets, a kid can't buy
$10 worth of hot dogs from the management.
After the game, the kids wait for the players.
They want to get autographs.
Sometimes the poor ballplayer has to push his
way through the crowd of kids.
Maybe you will be lucky.
Maybe you will get knocked down by Roger Maris.

Lesson 7.
THE BALLPARK VENDOR

See the vendor at the ballpark.
See him throw you your peanuts.
One, two, three rows behind you.
See him throw you your change.
One, two, three rows in front of you.
Ask him for a hot dog.
Watch him pass it along the row to you.
Count the fingerprints on your roll.
One, two, three, four, five, six, seven, eccch!
Also count the teeth marks on your hot dog.
One bicuspid. Two incisors. Four molars.
Now ask the vendor for some ice cream.
Also ask him for a straw to drink it with.

Lesson 8.
THE PARKING LOT

See the parking lot.
This is where you park your car.
See the attendant.
He sits and watches.
He watches kids steal your hub caps.
Also your antenna, spare tire and seat covers.
The parking lot attendant is very athletic.
He is a racing car driver.
Did you know you owned a racing car?
V-rroom! Screeech! Craashh!

The parking lot attendant will give your car a dent.
In return, you must give him a tip.
Sometimes a ball is hit out of the stadium.
Sometimes it lands in the parking lot.
Then you might bring home a souvenir of the game.
Like a shattered windshield.

Some time ago—mainly 33 issues back—we ran a selection of "Mother's Day Cards From Special People." Since then, we've been waiting for some reader to suggest that we run a selection of some "Father's Day Cards From Special People." Unfortunately, we have received no such letters. As a matter of fact, we've received hundreds of letters asking us *not* to run a selection of "Father's Day Cards From Special People," which is why we now proudly present this selection of

FATHER'S DAY CARDS

FROM SPECIAL PEOPLE

ARTIST: GEORGE WOODBRIDGE
WRITER: FRANK JACOBS

A Recipe for Dad!

Pot-au-père

First pour in kindness, wisdom, cheer,
Good fellowship and trust;
Then blend in patience, courage and
A viewpoint that is just;
A pinch of wit and merriment
Completes this loving snack;
I know that you'll enjoy it, Dad,
'Cause all these things you lack!

From a WEATHERMAN

To Dad—

I've clocked the motion of the wind,
And looked at my barometer;
I've watched the movements of the clouds,
And studied my thermometer;
No matter how I check my charts
And scan the skies of blue,
I know that I shall never find
A hot air mass like you!

From a FOREIGN CORRESPONDENT

To Dad—

I've covered riots in Berlin
    and fighting in Algiers;
I've tangled with Katanga tribes
    and dodged their poison spears;
I've seen the savage Red Chinese;
    I've braved the atom bomb;
But nothing, Dad, will ever beat
    Those fights you have with Mom!

From a LANDLORD

Dear
Old
Dad—

I think of you this Father's Day
And brush aside a tear;
I weep that we have been apart
Throughout this lonely year;
Although you're living hand-to-mouth,
Please hear my sad lament—
You'd still be living here with me
If you had paid your rent!

From a DOCTOR

To Dad—

Your pancreas is calcified;
Your fibroblasts are clotting;
And near your seventh vertebra
A spinal disc is rotting;
Your liver's twice its normal size;
One lung is turning gray;
I hope your life is filled with joy
This happy Father's Day!

From a PEACE CORPS MEMBER

Happy Father's Day!

When I was young, you bullied me
And filled me with defiance;
And so I joined the Peace Corps, Dad,
To get some self-reliance;
Out here, I've learned to be a man;
I'm more mature now, really;
I'm sending home my seven wives;
I hope you speak Swahili!

From a BUSINESSMAN

To Dad—

When I was just a little boy,
    You filled me with ambition—
And then you took me in the firm
    And gave me a position;
Secretly, behind your back,
    Your stock I have acquired;
I now own 51 per cent—
    And guess what, Dad?

You're fired!

MORE
MOVIE DIALOGUE WE'D LIKE TO HEAR

A COLLECTION OF "REVERSE CLICHES"
DESIGNED TO INJECT NEW LIFE INTO OLD "SURE-FIRE DIALOGUE"

ARTIST:
GEORGE
WOODBRIDGE

WRITER: HARRY PURVIS

I'm afraid I have some **bad news**, Mrs. Marshall! There's been a **crash**! Your **husband** was one of the **survivors**!

Yes, Danny and Marsha were **inseparable**! You never saw **one without the other**! But since her unexpected death, he's been having the **time of his life**!

I got **plenty** of use for a **loser**, Snivvly! You're **hired**!

MR. EE

You know honey . . . you look awfully **ugly** when you're angry!

GWOODBRIDGE

72

ON THE

BEACH

THWAT

David Berg has written this article in an attempt to recapture that great moment when he was nominated as "The All-Around Camper." In fact, he still believes he's "The All-Around Camper." But since Dave now weighs 230 pounds, the best that can be said is . . . he's an "ALL-ROUND Camper!" So here is his overweighted-with-laughs idea of

THE
LIGHTER
SIDE OF
SUMMER
CAMP

WRITER & ARTIST : DAVID BERG

Look at all this **equipment** I had to buy for her! **$300 worth**—and she'll probably never get to use **half** of it!

And don't forget the **name tapes** you gotta sew on every item!

OH, NO! I REFUSE! I will not spend weeks sewing name tapes on all these things!!

Then how the heck is she gonna know **her** stuff from the 200 **other** kids' in camp?!

Listen, Sheila! All the girls in camp will have their names on their things—so remember, whatever **doesn't** have a name on it is **yours**!!

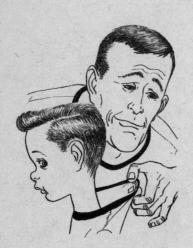

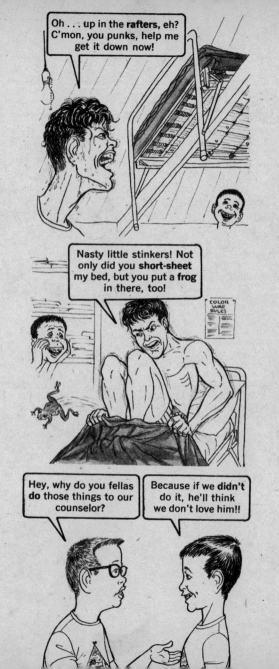

85

88

89

Let's go, boys! You know you've got to write a letter a day to your parents—

Yeah, but what do we **write**, Uncle Murray?

Okay! Everybody get ready, and I'll dictate . . .

"Dear Mom and Dad, I am fine. I hope you are the same . . ."

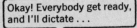

". . . and the food at camp is okay, but I get hungry around bedtime, so . . ."

". . . please keep sending those packages of food, like salami and cookies, because my provisions are running low! Your loving son, '. . .'"

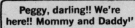

92

Antonio Prohias, who was forced to flee Cuba because he refused to become a "Castro Convertible", brings us another MAD installment of that friendly rivalry between the man in black and the man in white—better known as . . .

Some MAD Observations made while...

ON THE BEACH

IN THE TECHNOLOGY OF THE "COLD WAR"

ARTIST: JACK RICKARD
WRITER: PHIL HAHN

THE SPACE RACE

ALL SYSTEMS "GO"

RE-ENTRY PROBLEM

SECURITY MEASURES

OVER-FLIGHTS

CONDITION "RED"

SECURITY LEAK

MASSIVE RETALIATION

FALLOUT PROBLEM

IMPACT AREA

POLICE ACTION

DE-CONTAMINATION

OFF THE DEEP END

ARTIST: JACK RICKARD   WRITER: SERGIO ARAGONES

The characters in the comic strips do things that their real-life counterparts can only dream of doing. That's why we enjoy them so much. Through them, we can escape into a far more exciting and interesting world than the mundane one we live in. So even though they act completely unbelievable, we accept comic characters as if they were real living people. Which is why we feel it'd be such a shock . . .

IF COMIC STRIP CHARACTERS BEHAVED LIKE ORDINARY PEOPLE

ARTIST: WALLACE WOOD   WRITER: AL JAFFEE

If PEANUTS
behaved like real-life children

If DICK TRACY
behaved like an ordinary cop

If SUPERMAN
behaved like any normal guy

I CAN HARDLY WAIT TO GET TO LOIS'S APARTMENT...COCKTAILS, DINNER, SOFT MUSIC, AND... **ROWRRFF!!**

LOOK! HOW **HORRIBLE!!**

AN ARMY OF **KILLERS** WITH GUNS, KNIVES, AND BOMBS -- HEADING FOR CITY HALL!!

If POGO characters behaved like real animals

If BRINGING UP FATHER was about a real couple

2/22

©Fink Features Syndicate Inc.

If B.C. characters acted like real cavemen

121

If DENNIS THE MENACE had parents with normal patience

Enough is enough!!

THE CLASS PROGRAM

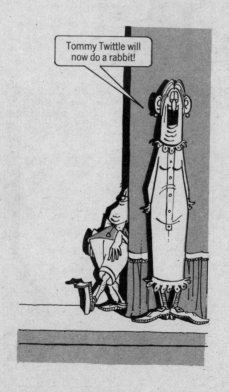

All right! Sally Smek will now do a rabbit!

HOORAY — YA-Y — BRAVO — BRAVO

<u>**WHERE'S THE FIRE DEPT.**</u>

Sergio Aragones, who recently arrived at MAD from Mexico, made his début with the hilarious "A MAD Look at the U.S. Space Effort." and is currently filling our margins with his delightful "Drawn-Out Dramas," now points his satirical pen at a usually un-funny U.S. phenomenon, and gives us

A MAD LOOK
AT
MOTORCYCLE
COPS

WRITER: ARTIST: SERGIO ARAGONES

POSTAL INTROSPECTION DEPT.

Today, it's possible for the ambitious clod to learn almost any skill, trade or profession by enrolling in one of the thousands of correspondence courses currently available. But strangely enough, no one has yet offered a much-needed course teaching psychoanalysis by mail, thus enabling the hapless neurotic to save the $25 an hour he now spends spewing out his woes to some overworked psychiatrist who probably isn't listening anyway. Rushing to the aid of these frenzied folk who can't cope with life, MAD now offers its own version of a home study course designed to accomplish . . .

PSYCHOANALYSIS BY MAIL=

ARTIST: JOE ORLANDO
WRITER: TOM KOCH

Session 1.
GENERAL EMOTIONAL STABILITY
(Score 5 points for each "Yes" Answer)

After concentrating hard on the illustration at left for 15 or 20 minutes, do you find yourself throwing a temper tantrum because you can't reach into the page and push the slanty side over to make the whole thing look more neat?___

When you saw this symbol, did you immediately look down at the bottom of the page for the footnote it refers to, and then burst into tears when there wasn't any?___

Are you filled with more frustration than you can bear because every pencil in the house has a broken point, leaving you with no possible way of filling in that awful white spot in the center of the circle?___

Did you stand on your head to make sense out of this one without stopping to realize that maybe it's right side up, and everything else in the world is upside down?___

Did this one make you giggle uncontrollably because you thought it looked like Jackie Gleason from the rear, bending over?___

Did this one compel you to go down and punch your laundryman in the mouth because you were mad over the fact that he knows what it means and you don't?___

Session 2.
ENVIRONMENTAL ADJUSTMENT
(Score 5 points for each "Yes" Answer)

1. Does the above illustration restore your faith in humanity because it proves that you are not the only one with sense enough to realize that a tree is the safest place in the world to live in?___

2. Don't you think the man in the picture would be happier if he'd picked a taller tree which was harder to climb, thus making it even more difficult for all the bad guys to get at him?___

3. Are you uncomfortable, even though you live alone on a desert island because you probably have a lot of snoopy neighbors living in Honolulu less than 1,300 miles away?___

4. Does it bother you that it is already tomorrow across the international dateline, and that the people on the other side think you're doing what you're doing right now yesterday?___

5. No matter how often you sell your house and move, do you always wind up with whole families of Communist spies living on both sides of you?___

6. When your phone rings, do you inform whoever is calling that they have the wrong number before they have a chance to pry into your personal affairs by saying something like, "Hello?"?___

Session 3.
MOTHER
(Score 5 points for each "Yes" Answer)

1. Does the above picture cause you to be more concerned about Mom's safety than about how much it is going to cost you to have her rocker repaired once the whole mess is over?___

2. Are you now working on two jobs, one day and one night, just so you can make more money to buy Mom some of the nice things that your rotten, no-good father always denied her?___

3. Do you cry yourself to sleep every night because the way your wife tucks you in and gives you your blanket to cuddle is not quite as comforting as the way Mom used to do it?___

4. Do you insist on having your mother accompany you everywhere you go because she is the only person capable of helping you cross the streets safely?___

5. Have you remained unmarried because you can't find a girl to take out who is 53 years old, has a weak worn face, and is willing to call you "Sonny"?___

6. Do you still telephone your Mother every night to have her sing you a lullaby even though you now live in San Diego and she lives in Bangor, Maine?___

Session 4.
THE INFERIORITY COMPLEX
(Score 5 points for each "Yes" Answer)

1. Are you humiliated beyond all reason because the ink blot above looks like nothing more than an ink blot to you, while you think that we think that you should think it looks like sex?___

2. Are you afraid that you will be blamed for spilling the ink that made the blot, and that shortly we'll be sending someone out to hit you for it?___

3. Do you avoid playing patty-cake with little kids because you're afraid they're better at it than you are?___

4. Do you confess to every axe murder because you hate to think of some criminal more worthy than yourself being electrocuted while you go scot-free?___

5. Whenever you pass a jewelry store with its clock-sign reading 8:20, do you unconsciously set your watch for that time, assuming that the jeweler must know the correct time and that you were the one who made the mistake and went out to lunch four hours early?___

6. Do you send Mom a note of apology instead of a card every Mother's Day because you know how she must feel having a mess like you for a kid?___

Session 5.
FETISHES

(Score 5 points for each "Yes" Answer)

1. Even though you live alone, have you been forced to buy a 14-room house because you need at least 13 rooms to store your collection of old bottle caps?___

2. At a party, do you sit quietly until everyone else gets too plastered to notice you, and then start rummaging feverishly through bureau drawers?___

3. When your wife suggests a picnic, do you insist on holding it near the City Dump so you can scrounge through the rubbish while the rest of the family is eating?___

4. Have you given away all your slipover sweaters because you can't figure out how to put one on without taking off your hat?___

5. Do you stock up on more canned goods than you can possibly eat just because you love to look at the pictures on the labels?___

6. Do you hide spare rolls of string in chandeliers, under beds and other secret places around your house, just so you won't get caught short in case your wife finds your regular supply and throws it out?___

Session 6.
COMPULSIONS
(Score 5 points for each "Yes" Answer)

1. When you see these numbers, do you rush to the library to see what subject it covers under the Dewey Decimal System, instead of rushing to take your temperature the way a normal person would?___

2. Are you in financial trouble because you can't resist saving your pay envelope every week, and throwing away the check inside?___

3. When you receive an engraved invitation to a five o'clock cocktail party, do you show up at both five A.M. and again at five P.M., just to play it safe?___

4. Have you stayed in your room with the door locked ever since you stepped on a crack in the sidewalk two years ago last summer?___

5. Do you have a lot of auto accidents because you are afraid that glancing at the road occasionally would cause you to lose count of the number of telephone poles you're driving past?___

6. Do you have more dreams about Harold Stassen than other people seem to?

Session 7.
TELEPHONE PSYCHOSIS

(Score 5 points for each "Yes" Answer)

1. Does the mere sight of the man in the picture fill you with joyous anticipation because you're certain he'll call you up any minute now, and you can hardly wait to talk to him even though you have no idea who he is?____

2. Do you sometimes wish that you had two phones with different numbers so you could call yourself up and have somebody convivial to chat with?____

3. Have you been calling up wrong numbers and saying "Guess who this is?" for so long that they know who it is by now?____

4. Do you carry on long conversations with the girl on the phone who gives you the correct time even though she seems to have a one-track mind that causes her to reply to everything you say by telling you what time it is?____

5. Is it your idea of a big time to call up every grocer in town and order huge quantities of food to be delivered to addresses that don't exist?____

6. After you've called everyone you can think of, do you while away many happy hours just sitting there listening to the dial tone?____

Session 8.
TELEVISION PSYCHOSIS

(Score 5 points for each "Yes" Answer)

1. Do you wish you had a TV set that could bring in all 13 channels at the same time so you wouldn't ever, ever, ever have to miss any show, no matter how lousy it was?___

2. Do you toss and turn all night because the announcer on the "11 O'Clock News" always tells you to rush right out and buy "Dristan," and you can't because the drug store in your neighborhood closes at 10:30?___

3. Is your greatest pride in life the fact that you stopped using that greasy kid stuff on your hair even before the TV people told you to?___

4. Do you always wear your best suit while watching TV because you assume that the people on the screen can see you and you don't want to be considered a slob?___

5. Is the greatest thing you fear about a Communist take-over the possibility that you might be sent to Siberia, which you understand is in a fringe reception area?___

6. Do you sometimes get out of bed at 4 A.M. after all the TV stations have gone off the air, and still get a lot of pleasure out of turning on the set and just watching the snow on the screen?___

Session 9.

FRUSTRATIONS

(Score 5 points for each "Yes" Answer)

1. Do you beat up your wife and children every evening just because there's no one left to beat up after you've spent the day beating up your co-workers and customers?____

2. Have you ever had the triumphant dream that you stalked and killed a lyrfimstrdl, and then suffered a terrible let-down when you awoke and found it wasn't even listed in the dictionary?____

3. Are you frustrated beyond endurance because you've been writing down every joke you hear and mailing them to Ed Sullivan, and he still doesn't laugh?____

4. Do you ever dream that you've just met a beautiful blonde, and then get mad because the alarm clock goes off before you've had a chance to get her name and phone number?____

5. Do you fly into a towering rage every time you watch "Gunsmoke" because Chester won't stop limping no matter how many letters of protest you write to the network?____

6. Do you hate your mother and father because you wanted to be an African pygmy when you grew up and they wouldn't let you?____

Session 10.

SCORING AND RECOMMENDED THERAPY

If your score is 0-25, you have no problems because you either didn't go to school at all, or somehow managed to skip the grades where they taught reading.

If your score is 30-35, you should buy a dictionary, read it cover to cover, and then take this quiz over again on the off-chance that the new results will prove you to be less of a nut than you really are.

If your score is 60-85, just stay under your bed and keep re-reading the label on the bottom of the box spring until you feel better.

if your score is 90-115, don't clutter up your mind with tests like these. You need all the mental power you can muster just to remember who you are in case anybody should ever ask.

If your score is 120-145, you are almost completely unglued and should immediately send us an additional $150 for our "Advanced Course" while you still have sense enough to remember where you put your check book.

If your score is 150-175, don't send us the $150. Use it to have bars installed in all your windows to protect your neighbors from what you are most likely to do next.

If your score is 180-205, quit your job immediately and have as much fun as you can before they catch up with you.

If your score is 210-235, cultivate the ability to hold your breath for long periods of time so you will be in shape to move to the bottom of the ocean in case your condition worsens.

If your score is 240-270, don't call us. We'll arrange for the nearest sanitarium to call you.

Antonio Prohias, who was forced to flee Cuba because he refused to become a "Castro Convertible", brings us another MAD installment of that friendly rivalry between the man in black and the man in white—better known as . . .

PATENT PANNING DEPT.

Because progress brings change, and changes are always supposed to be for the better, Man sometimes forgets to look back to see exactly how far he has progressed, and from where. Which is exactly what this article is all about. And so here we go with ...

MAD'S
REPORT ON

ARTIST: BOB CLARKE   WRITER: DICK DE BARTOLO

Electric fan of yesterday, even though electrified, could only circulate "hot" air, and gave no relief to hay fever.

PROGRESS

The modern air conditioner actually "cools" hot air, then circulates it. In addition, it also dehumidifies and even filters the air. It stops hay fever . . . starts pneumonia.

Here is a typical old-fashioned wood pencil. It wasn't very versatile, and could only be depended on to write and erase.

Man put his ingenious mind to work in an effort to improve the pencil, and today we have the miracle known as "liquid

Old alarm clock was ugly, had to be wound, ticked loudly, rang harshly. Blasted awake, sleeper did not feel rested.

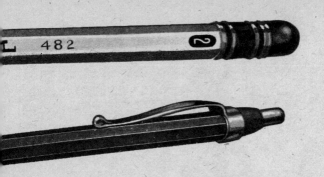

lead." Unlike its predecessor, this versatile "liquid lead" pencil not only writes, it skips, leaks, jams and runs dry.

Modern electric clock-radio is sleek and trim. No ticking bothers sleeper. When it's time to get up, gentle soothing music plays. Sleeper wakes up rested, mainly because that soothing music puts him back to sleep for an extra 7 hours.

Old portable radios were heavy and bulky, could only boast of fine tone and rugged, complicated hand-wired circuits.

Old fashioned manually-operated typewriter was awkward in use—held down speed of even the most experienced typists.

Modern tiny transistor portable radio slips into a shirt pocket easily. Also slips out easily, especially when you bend over. But printed circuits are a breeze to repair. You merely replace whole insides. This costs more than a brand new radio. One-inch hi-fi speaker has unusual tone. Tinny.

Modern high-speed electric typewriter is the answer to any typist's dream. Now, even a novice can use it to type 80, 90, even 100 errors and strike-overs a XXXXXXXX minute.

Old style box camera offered few advantages such as focus, shutter speed and lens settings. It merely took pictures.

Old fashioned printing press could only reproduce one page at a time. Many famous works were printed on such presses.

Modern camera offers many advantages. Amateur photo bugs can now ruin pictures with over 400 wrong settings, and professionals can discover many additional wrong settings.

Modern-day printing press turns out thousands of pages per second. Printing methods have progressed a long way—but we seem to be moving ever backward in the *things* we print.

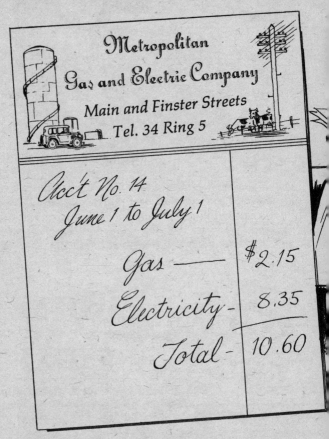

Metropolitan

Gas and Electric Company

Main and Finster Streets

Tel. 34 Ring 5

Acc't No. 14
June 1 to July 1

Gas —	$2.15
Electricity —	8.35
Total —	10.60

In days gone by, monthly bills and statements were figured mentally and written by hand. Petty errors were often made.

Metropolitan Gas and Electric Company
Main and Finster Streets

ACCOUNT NO: 289-56-735 XP 11

BILLING PERIOD: June 1 to July 1

GAS	$2.15
ELECTRICITY	8.35
TOTAL DUE:	$11,000.50

◄ PAY THIS FIGURE IMMEDIATELY OR SERVICE WILL BE DISCONTINUED

DO NOT FOLD, STAPLE OR BEND. RETURN WITH PAYMENT

Modern billing machines electronically calculate and print monthly statements. Petty errors have been eliminated. Now *major* errors are made—usually runnning into the thousands.

BRAIN SURGERY

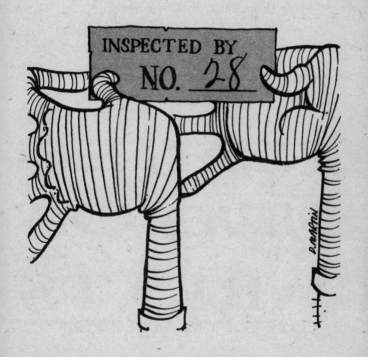

INSPECTED BY

NO. 28

The relationship between Parents and their Little Kids can be summed up in one word: Aggravation! Yessiree, Parents sure give their Little Kids plenty of aggravation! You'll see exactly what we mean in this article by Dave Berg . . . who gave his Little Kids plenty of aggravation while researching:

THE LIGHTER SIDE OF PARENTS
(OF LITTLE KIDS)

WRITER & ARTIST: DAVID BERG

169

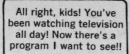

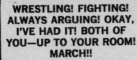
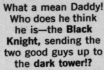

WRESTLING! FIGHTING! ALWAYS ARGUING! OKAY, I'VE HAD IT! BOTH OF YOU—UP TO YOUR ROOM! MARCH!!

What a mean Daddy! Who does he think he is—the **Black Knight**, sending the two good guys up to the **dark tower**!?

Yeah! We oughta report him to the **Society for the Prevention of Cruelty to Children!** Imagine—sending two poor kids up to their **room** alla time for **punishment**!!

Oh, Jerry, I'm so glad you're home! I've had such a terrible day with Randi. It seems that she lost a **tooth** yesterday, and we forgot to put **money** from **"The Good Fairy"** under her pillow. Well, I tell you, there's been such crying and carrying-on all day long—

The poor kid! Let's **make it up** to her! Get me some of that **gold glitter paint** your cub scout den was using—and one of her **dolls** . . .

See—with the gold paint on the doll's shoes, I'm making **fairy footprints** from the window to Randi's bed . . .

Just wait till your **father** comes home and I tell him what you've done! Boy, is he gonna give **you** a licking!

Ain't **you scared?**

Naahh! I know how to handle **them!** All I have to do is get to my Daddy **first—** before he comes into the house!

Daddy! **Daddy!** I've got the **bestest Daddy** in the **whole world!** All the **other** kids are **jealous** 'cause my Daddy is better'n **their** Daddies!!

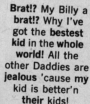

So you're **home!** Well, let me tell you about this **brat** of yours—

Brat!? My Billy a **brat!?** Why I've got the **bestest** kid in the **whole** world! All the **other** Daddies are **jealous** 'cause my kid is better'n **their** kids!

You don't appreciate what a **good mother** I am! Look at this beautiful spotless house I've given you! And this lovely room you've got!

No! No! Don't touch those toys! I've just spent an hour straightening them up!

No! No! You can't play in the den! I've just had the floor waxed!

C'mon, Stu! Let's go over to Mark's house! His mom don't care what kind of a mess we make! She's a terrible mother!!

From time immemorial, graduating students have felt that there are no longer any opportunities left to make one's fortune. They've said things like: "Everything's been invented, or discovered, or cashed-in on . . . and there are no new frontiers left to conquer!" Well, we say things like: "Baloney!" Where would Thomas A. Edison, Jonas Salk and Hugh Hefner be if they'd believed that? Mainly, opportunities are all around us. Mankind is constantly beset with problems. All you have to do is open your eyes, solve these problems, and you'll come up with profitable ideas like . . .

NEW OPPORTUNITIES FOR RECENT GRADS

ARTIST: JACK RICKARD   WRITER: AL JAFFEE

THE PROBLEM: Gigantic Parking Lots

Anyone who has left a car in an outer aisle of a typical 32 acre modern shopping center or recreation area parking lot knows how exhausting the trips in and out can be.

YOUR OPPORTUNITY: Parking Lot Shuttle Bus

Set up a "Shuttle Bus Service" from the outer fringes of the parking lot to the stores, bowling alley or ball park. You could charge according to aisle, or number of bundles.

THE PROBLEM: Doctors' Answering Service

If you've ever called your family doctor in an emergency, only to reach his "answering service," you know the panic and frustration of being informed that he's not available.

YOUR OPPORTUNITY: Doctors' Finder Service

Organize a group of professional "Doctor Tailers." Assign each to a doctor. When customer calls your service, his doctor is contacted personally, and he can't squirm out.

THE PROBLEM: Sitter Anxiety

All parents are apprehensive about what really goes on after they leave their little dears in the care of a baby sitter. Rumors of wild parties and abused kids are heard.

YOUR OPPORTUNITY: Sitter Spy Patrol

THIS HOUSE PROTECTED BY SITTER SPY SERVICE

"Sitter Spy Patrol" services a list of member-clients who signal every time they go out. Their sitter is aware that you might drop in for a spot check at anytime, and behaves.

THE PROBLEM: Cleaning Up For The Cleaning Girl

Many housewives frantically "straighten up a bit" before regular cleaning-girl arrives, claiming then she'll only have the important work to do. Actually, housewife would rather die than let girl know what a slob she really is.

YOUR OPPORTUNITY: Pre-Cleaning-Girl Service

Start a "Pre-Cleaning-Girl Cleaning Service" with bonded and insured girls that have passkeys to customers' homes. They sneak in and pre-clean before regular girl arrives. Housewife never sees "pre-cleaner"—can't be embarrassed.

THE PROBLEM: Long Waiting Lines

With population explosion comes over-crowding everywhere. Lines for hit shows, ball games—even at banks and barber shops grow longer and longer and waiting has its problems.

YOUR OPPORTUNITY: Place-Keeping Service

People who have invested a lot of time waiting on a line will welcome your service so they can solve problems like trips to rest rooms and starvation—without losing place.

THE PROBLEM: Unassembled Purchases

Buying unassembled article means the customer is working for the manufacturer and doesn't know it. He saves labor costs of assembly, and customer ends up botching the job.

THE SOLUTION: Visiting Assembly Service

Organize a "Visiting Assembly Service." For small kickback, stores will insert your message in each box. When frantic customer calls for help . . . you step in and save the day.

THE PROBLEM: Growing Trading Stamp Nuisance

Growing numbers of housewives are becoming disenchanted with trading stamps. They are beginning to realize that they're really paying for the gifts — plus salaries, rents and profits of the stamp companies and their ad agencies.

YOUR SOLUTION: Trading Stamp Trading Store

Open store that gives groceries for trading stamps. After all, that's what housewives needed in first place. Then, redeem stamps for gifts, open gift-shop, sell gifts, and re-stock groceries with part of gift-shop's huge profits.

THE PROBLEM: Family Disputes

In any American home, when you find dissension, arguing, bitterness and hatred, you'll probably find the same old cause for it . . . mainly: who's gonna take out the garbage?

YOUR OPPORTUNITY: Garbage Take-Out Service

Your service would call daily and carry the garbage from the house can to the outside can. Every husband would be thrilled to pay for bringing happiness back to his home.

ON
THE
BOARDWALK